RESPONDING TO LITERATURE

WRITING & THINKING ACTIVITIES

Sandra M. Simons, Ph.D.

SPRING·STREET·PRESS

2606 Spring Blvd., Eugene, OR 97405

Cover design: Jean McCandless, Los Altos Hills CA
Page design: Gene Floersch, Beach Studies, Inc., Melbourne Beach FL

CONTENTS

LITERARY FORMS

Historical Fiction

Nonfiction

Autobiography & Biography

Play

Folk Tale

TO THE TEACHER

Responding to Literature: Writing and Thinking Activities is a valuable teaching aid to use in in your reading or language arts classroom. It contains 75 reproducible reading **Response Activities** that may be used with any reading selection. There are also 8 reproducible **Record Keeping Charts** to assist you in monitoring and managing students' reading. The **Response Activities** may be used in a variety of ways to adapt to your reading curriculum and teaching style as well as to the abilities and learning styles of your students.

INSTRUCTIONAL FEATURES

Response Activities enhance your reading instruction by:

- integrating reading, writing, and thinking

- providing open-ended assignments that encourage students to express their own reactions to and opinions about what they read

- requiring students to think critically about what they have read

- encouraging creative responses that extend thinking beyond the reading selection

- motivating students to derive personal meaning from their reading

Response Activities help you meet the needs of all students by:

- providing a variety of activities to accommodate students with different learning styles and varying abilities

- providing nonthreatening, motivating activities that the at-risk student can and will do

- providing opportunities for Limited-English-Proficiency students to participate in class with personal responses to what they read

ORGANIZATIONAL FEATURES

Record Keeping Charts help you monitor students' reading by:

- providing a variety of simple formats that students can use to record what they read

- encouraging students to take responsibility for keeping track of their own reading

Response Activities supplement any reading program you are using. Use them with:

- **literature-based reading programs**

     The response activities are designed to be used with any literature selection.

     Assign response activities to individuals, to a small group of students reading the same book, or to the entire class. If the entire class reads the same book, you may have all students complete the same activity or assign activities based on each student's need, ability, and learning style.

     Augment your instruction by using response activities that focus on literary elements or genre. For example, if you are teaching characterization, you may assign one of the twenty response activities that focus on character.

- **independent reading programs**

     The generic nature of the activities makes them applicable to any book students choose.

     The variety of activities enables you to make assignments that are appropriate for the each student's ability and learning style.

     The response activity format is easy for students to complete independently.

- **basal reading programs**

     Use response activities to supplement workbook activities in your basal reading program.

Response activities accommodate your teaching style. Use them with:

- **cooperative group instuction**

     The response activities may be used as a basis for small group assignments and discussions.

- **whole-class instruction**

- **individualized instruction**

THE RESPONSE ACTIVITY PAGE

Each **Response Activity** copying master has a clear, consistent format that enables students to do the activity independently and lets you know at a glance what students are doing.

To help you select the **Response Activity** that best fits with your instructional program, the book symbol displays the curriculum focus of the activity. The top label indicates the general instructional area: literary elements, literary forms, or general response. The lower label identifies the specific literary genre or literary element.

The mask symbol indicates that the writing activity requires that students write from a point of view other than their own.

Easy-to-read directions thoroughly explain the assignment. For each writing activity, the directions alert students to the writing task, the purpose for writing, the role students will take as writers, their audience, and the format of the writing.

This symbol is a signal to students that they will revise and edit their writing and then copy it onto a clean sheet of paper.

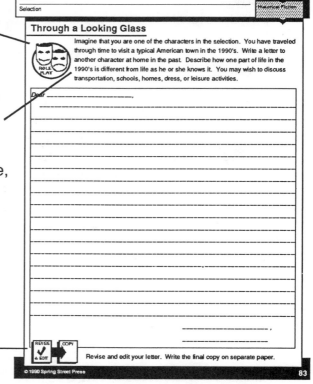

 When this symbol appears, it indicates that students are to write their drafts and final versions on separate paper.

THE TEACHER'S PAGE

On the back of each copying master is an easy reference to help you select the page that is most appropriate for your instructional needs and the students' abilities and learning styles.

The activity label at the top of the page lets you see at a glance the task students will complete.

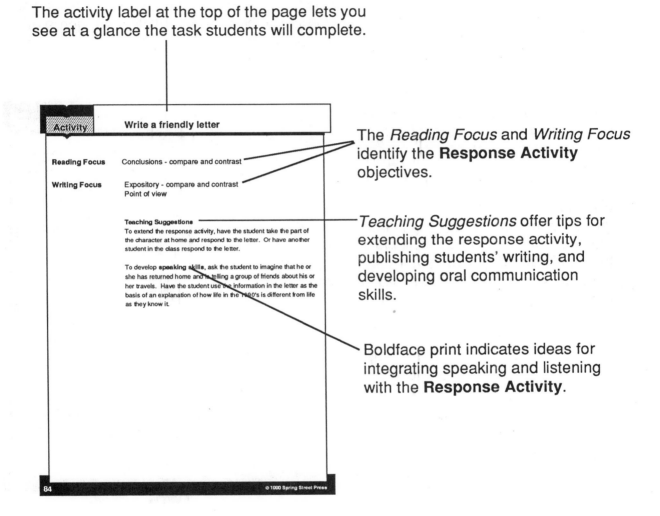

The *Reading Focus* and *Writing Focus* identify the **Response Activity** objectives.

Teaching Suggestions offer tips for extending the response activity, publishing students' writing, and developing oral communication skills.

Boldface print indicates ideas for integrating speaking and listening with the **Response Activity**.

Where in the World?

Write an acrostic poem to describe the setting of the selection.   In an acrostic, the first letters of each line form a word, when read from top to bottom.   The word names the topic of the poem. The example shows an acrostic about the setting of a science fiction story.

Moon
Outstanding sight
Of the
Night skies

For your topic, choose one word that describes or names the setting of your favorite part of the selection. Write your topic on the line above the chart.

Next complete the chart. List words you might use to go with each letter in the topic. Use the back of the page if you need more space.

TOPIC _____

Letters	Words

Write the letters of the topic down the page. Then write your poem. Remember that your poem should describe the setting.

_____   _____

_____   _____

_____   _____

_____   _____

_____   _____

_____   _____

_____   _____

Revise and edit your poem. Write the final copy on separate paper.

Reading Focus   Setting

Writing Focus   Description - poem

Teaching Suggestions
Some students may wish to illustrate their poems and display them on a bulletin board for students' work.

Take a New Look

Rewrite a scene from the selection as if it occurred in a different setting. Choose one of the times or places in the box. You may use both a different time and place if you wish.

- one hundred years in the future
- two hundred years in the past
- in a village in northern Alaska
- in your own city
- in a crowded city

- on another planet
- in another country
- in a jungle
- in your school yard
- on a farm

REVISE
✓
& EDIT

COPY

Revise and edit your writing. Write the final copy on separate paper.

Reading Focus   Setting
                       Summary

Writing Focus   Narrative - story scene

Teaching Suggestions
Encourage students to choose a scene that would be be affected by a change in setting. For example, a camping trip set in the Rocky Mountains would change if it took place in the jungle.

Imagine That!

ROLE PLAY

Follow the directions to complete the map.
- Imagine that you are a character in your favorite part of the story. Fill in the box at the bottom of the page to tell who you are, where you are, and when you are there.
- Complete the rest of the map with words and phrases to describe what you see, hear, smell, feel, and taste. Use words and phrases from the selection as well as some of your own.

What do you see?

What do you hear?

What do you feel?

What do you taste?

What do you smell?

Character: _____
Setting: When and Where?

WORK ON → NEW PAPER

On separate paper, write a paragraph to describe the setting from the character's point of view. Use decriptive details to awaken the reader's senses and create a vivid picture.

Write a descriptive paragraph

Reading Focus   Setting

Writing Focus   Description - sensory details
                           Point of view

Teaching Suggestions

To develop **speaking skills**, have the student read aloud his or her description to a small group. As classmates listen, they are to write down the senses that the writer awakens in them. Then have the listeners give feedback to the writer in which they explain which sensory details in the paragraph are most effective.

Name

Selection

Picture This!

Illustrate the setting of the part of the selection you liked best. Draw your picture in the box.

Write a paragraph to describe the setting to someone you think would enjoy reading the selection. Use descriptive details and colorful words to create a vivid picture in the mind of your reader.

_____

_____

_____

_____

_____

_____

_____

_____

_____

_____

_____

_____

Reading Focus   Setting

Writing Focus   Description - paragraph

Teaching Suggestions

To develop **speaking skills** and to obtain feedback for revising their paragraphs, have students read aloud their descriptions to a classmate or family member. The listener will draw the picture that the words create in his or her mind. The writer will then use the picture to revise the description.

How Do You Feel?

The mood of a selection is the feeling that it creates in the reader. Writers establish mood with words and phrases they use to describe setting, characters, and events. For example, *dark shadows* and *blood-curdling scream* create a feeling of fear.

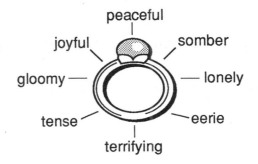

Think about your favorite part of the selection and the feeling you had as you read it. Write this feeling in the center of the mood ring. Then scan that part of the selection to find words and phrases that the writer uses to create this mood. Write them in a cluster around the ring.

MOOD

Think of other words and phrases you would use to create the same mood. Add them to the cluster.

On separate paper, write a paragraph in which you create the same mood as the writer created. Use some of the words and phrases from your cluster.

© 1990 Spring Street Press

Reading Focus   Mood

Writing Focus   Description - paragraph

Teaching Suggestions
To develop **speaking skills,** have students read aloud their paragraphs and have the audience identify the mood that the writer is creating.

Name _____

Selection _____

Get the Message

What is the theme, or author's message? _____

_____

Plan and write a short story with the same message. Begin by completing the story plan.

SETTING   DESCRIBE WHEN AND WHERE THE STORY TAKES PLACE.

_____

_____

CHARACTERS   NAME EACH MAJOR CHARACTER.

_____

PROBLEM   EXPLAIN THE PROBLEM.

_____

_____

_____

RISING ACTION   LIST THE MAIN EVENTS THAT LEAD TO THE SOLUTION OF THE PROBLEM.

• _____

_____

• _____

_____

• _____

_____

• _____

_____

SOLUTION   EXPLAIN HOW THE PROBLEM IS SOLVED.

_____

_____

_____

WORK ON → NEW PAPER

Write your story on separate paper.

Write a short story

Reading Focus	Theme
Writing Focus	Narrative - short story

Teaching Suggestions

To develop **speaking skills**, have students be storytellers and tell their stories to the class. Encourage students to rehearse their stories before they present them.

Got the Picture?

Design a book cover that illustrates the writer's theme, or message. Be sure to include the title and author of the selection on your cover.

In a sentence or two, state the writer's theme, or message.

_____

_____

_____

Design a book jacket cover

Reading Focus   Theme

Writing Focus   Expository - main idea statement

Teaching Suggestions

Have students use the page to plan and sketch their illustrations and draw their final designs on art paper.

To extend the response activity, have students write a story summary for the flaps on a book jacket flap.

In So Many Words

Be an advertising writer who composes the information for the flaps of book jackets. Write the copy for a book jacket for your selection. Remember that your job is to tell enough about the story to interest a reader but not to tell how events turn out or give away the ending. Introduce the characters, tell the problem, and hint at the exciting events that will follow.

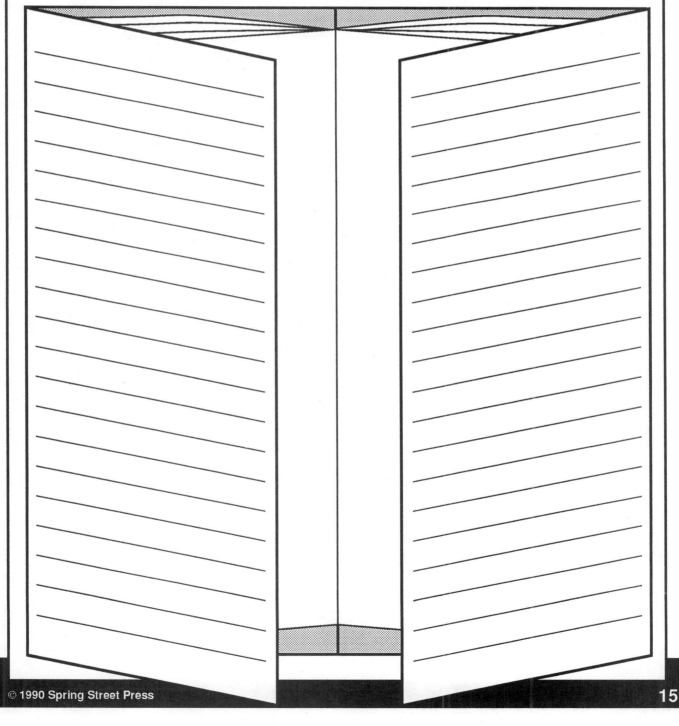

Write copy for a book jacket

Reading Focus   Plot - problem

Writing Focus   Narrative - summary

Teaching Suggestions
Suggest that students make book jackets for their books. Have them fold art paper into a book jacket, design a cover, and write the final copy of their summaries on the flaps. Display book jackets.

Sum It Up

Complete the plot map. Then use the information in the map to write a summary of the selection.

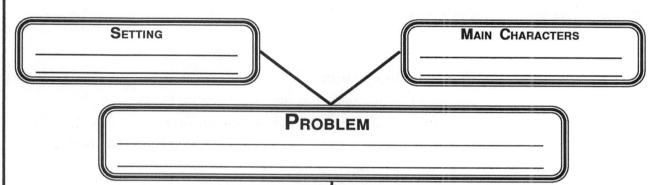

SETTING
_____
_____

MAIN CHARACTERS
_____
_____

PROBLEM
_____
_____

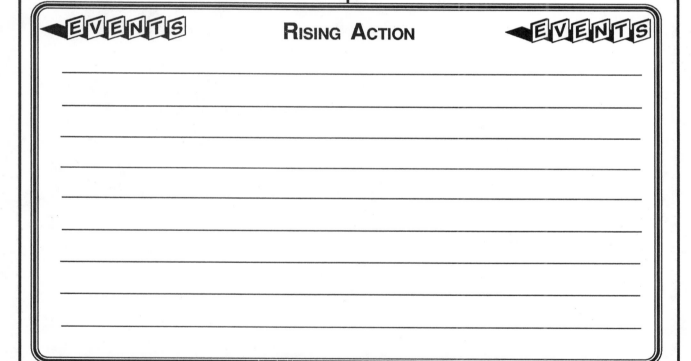

EVENTS   **RISING ACTION**   **EVENTS**
_____
_____
_____
_____
_____
_____
_____
_____

SOLUTION
_____
_____

WORK ON → NEW PAPER

Write your summary on separate paper.

Map and summarize a selection

Reading Focus   Plot - elements

Writing Focus   Exposition - plot summary

Teaching Suggestions

Review that a plot summary includes only the most important events that lead to the solution of the problem.

To develop **speaking skills**, have students use their plot maps to give two-minute book talks. Remind students that a book talk should interest others in reading the book; therefore, they should not to tell the solution to the problem nor should they reveal the most exciting events and the climax.

Literature Is News That *Stays* News

Write two short news stories about events or characters in the selection. Write your stories on the newspaper front page below. Then write a headline for each story.

Literature News

Revise and edit your news stories. Write the final copies on separate paper.

Reading Focus   Plot - main events

Writing Focus   Narrative - news stories

Teaching Suggestions
Have students create their own newspaper front page on large paper and write the final versions of their stories on the page. Some students may wish to add pictures or more news stories to their front pages. Display the newspaper pages on a bullein board of students' work.

Create a Comic Strip

Retell your favorite scene in the selection in a comic strip. Illustrate four important events that tell what happened. In the oval above each picture, write what a character says. Then draw a line to connect the speech bubble with the character who is speaking.

Create a comic strip

Reading Focus   Plot - main events

Writing Focus   Narrative - dialogue

Teaching Suggestions
Students may wish to use the page for sketches and draw their final illustrations on art paper. Display comic strips on a bulletin board of students' work.

It Happened Like This ...

ROLE PLAY

Imagine that the national news is covering the most exciting event in the selection. Be one of the characters involved in the event. Tell the news reporter what happened.

Who was involved? _____

_____

When did it happen? _____

Where did it happen? _____

What happened? _____

_____

_____

_____

_____

_____

_____

_____

_____

_____

_____

_____

_____

_____

_____

_____

_____

Retell an exciting event

Reading Focus   Plot - exciting event

Writing Focus   Narrative - sequence
Point of view

Teaching Suggestions
To develop **speaking skills**, have the student take the role of the news reporter and present a news broadcast in which he or she reports the event.

Chrono-Log

Complete the chrono-log with the eight most important events that retell the story. Arrange the events in chronological order.   Then use your chrono-log to write a summary of the story.

Event 1

Event 2

Event 3

Event 4

Event 5

Event 6

Event 7

Event 8

WORK ON   NEW PAPER   Write your summary on separate paper.

Map and summarize main events

Reading Focus	Plot - main events Sequence
Writing Focus	Narrative - sequence

Teaching Suggestions

Encourage students to combine sentences from their chrono-logs as they write their summaries.

To develop **speaking skills**, have students give book talks in which they tell the events in the first half of their chrono-logs. Remind students that their book talks should interest the audience in reading the selection and should not give away the story ending or reveal the climax.

Name

Selection

Put an End to It

Imagine that you are a TV screen writer. A producer has decided to make a TV movie out of the selection; however, she doesn't like its ending. She has asked you to create a new ending. Write an ending that is a logical solution to the story problem and fits with events in the story.

Revise and edit your story ending. Write the final copy on separate paper.

Write a story ending

Reading Focus   Predictions

Writing Focus   Narrative - story ending

Teaching Suggestions
To develop **speaking skills**, have the student briefly retell the main events of the story, except the ending. Then have the student present both endings and ask the audience to decide which ending they prefer.

For a Song

A ballad is a song that tells a story. Write a ballad that retells the story you read. Rewrite the words to a song you already know or make up your own melody. Your ballad should have at least three verses that are each four lines.

Revise and edit your ballad. Write the final copy on separate paper.

Write a ballad

Reading Focus   Plot - summary

Writing Focus   Narrative - poem

Teaching Suggestions
Some students may enjoy tape recording their ballads or performing them for the class.

Send a Post Card

Be the main character of your selection. Write a post card to a friend telling what you have been doing. Your note should summarize the story problem or a main event in the story. Use the box to write your first draft and make revisions. Then write your final copy in the post card below.

Post Card

Write a post card note

Reading Focus   Plot - problem and main event

Writing Focus   Narrative - summary
                      Point of view

Teaching Suggestions

To extend the activity, have students design their own post cards on tagboard. On one side of the post card, have students draw a picture that relates to the selection. On the other, have them write the final copy of their notes.

Name _____

Selection _____

Extra! Extra!

Be a newspaper reporter. Write a news story to report a newsworthy event from the selection. Remember that the lead paragprah of a news story tells the important facts - who, what, when, where, and why. The paragraphs that follow relate details about what happened. The headline states the main idea.

Daily News

Revise and edit your news story. Write the final copy on separate paper.

Write a news story

Reading Focus   Plot - main event

Writing Focus   Narrative - news story

Teaching Suggestions
To develop **speaking skills,** have the students present a news
broadcast in which they report their stories.

Words to Wear

Create slogans for tee shirts for two of the characters in the selection. Each slogan should tell something about the character's personality, actions, or attitudes. After writing the slogan on each shirt, explain how the slogan applies to the character.

Character: _____

Explain why the slogan is appropriate for the character.

_____
_____
_____
_____
_____
_____
_____
_____

Character: _____

Explain why the slogan is appropriate for the character.

_____
_____
_____
_____
_____
_____
_____
_____
_____
_____

Write tee shirt slogans

Reading Focus   Conclusions - character traits and motives

Writing Focus   Expository - explanation

Teaching Suggestions

Before students begin, brainstorm possible slogans that would be appropriate for fairy tale characters. For example, a slogan for a tee shirt for a dwarf in *Snow White* might be "Little People Have Big Hearts," and one for Cinderella's stepmother might be "Bigfoot Lives."

Name

Selection

Write Your Pen Pal

Be the main character in your selection. Write a friendly letter to your pen pal, who is a character in another selection you have read. In the letter discuss how you are like one another. You may wish to explain how your living circumstances are alike, tell how your problems are similar, or discuss interests that you have in common.

ROLE PLAY

_____

_____

Dear _____,

_____

_____

_____

_____

_____

_____

_____

_____

_____

_____

_____

_____

_____

_____

_____

_____

_____

Yours truly,

_____

Revise and edit your letter. Write the final copy on separate paper.

Write a friendly letter

Reading Focus   Comparisons - characters

Writing Focus   Expository - comparison
Point of view

Teaching Suggestions
To extend the activity, have students take the role of the character
to whom they have written and write a letter of response.

What a Character!

Complete the chart to describe three characters in the selection.

CHARACTER _____

Of whom does the character remind you? _____

In two sentences, describe the most interesting thing about the character.

_____

_____

_____

_____

CHARACTER _____

Of whom does the character remind you? _____

In two sentences, describe the most interesting thing about the character.

_____

_____

_____

_____

CHARACTER _____

Of whom does the character remind you? _____

In two sentences, describe the most interesting thing about the character.

_____

_____

_____

_____

Describe characters

Reading Focus   Conclusions - character traits and motives
Judgments

Writing Focus   Description - character

Teaching Suggestions
Explain to students that when they are deciding of whom the
character reminds them, they should think of people they know
including their relatives, friends, and classmates.

Lights! Camera! Action!

Imagine that you are a television talk show host. Your job is to interview the main character of the selection. Write three questions you will ask him or her. Remember to ask questions that will interest your audience and will help them get to know the character.

ROLE PLAY

CHARACTER YOU WILL INTERVIEW _____

QUESTION 1 _____

_____

QUESTION 2 _____

_____

QUESTION 3 _____

_____

Be the character. Answer each of the questions.

ANSWER 1 _____

_____

_____

ANSWER 2 _____

_____

_____

ANSWER 3 _____

_____

_____

Plan a TV talk show

Reading Focus   Conclusions - character traits and motives

Writing Focus   Expository - explanation

Teaching Suggestions
To develop **speaking skills**, have students work in pairs to present their talk show inteviews. A student who has not read the selection may take the part of the talk show host.

Create a Coat of Arms

At one time in history, coats of arms were worn to identify people. Symbols on the coat of arms represented an outstanding quality or an important event in the life of the owner. Design a coat of arms for one of the characters in the selection. One half of the design should symbolize the character's best quality; the other half, an important event in the character's life. Then write an explanation of your design. Use the back of this page.

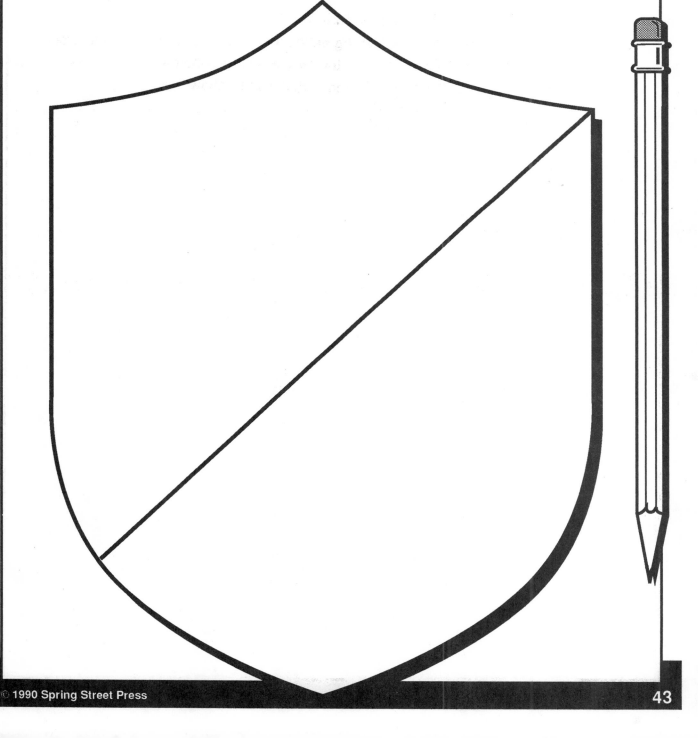

Design a coat of arms

Reading Focus   Conclusions - character traits
Main idea

Writing Focus   Expository - explanation

Teaching Suggestions

Explain how symbols may represent character traits. For example, a barbell might symbolize strength or a flower, happiness. Encourage students to think of original symbols. Then suggest that students write their explanations in a two-paragraph format: one paragraph to explain each half of the coat of arms.

Some students may wish to draw their final coats of arms on art paper.

To develop **speaking skills,** have students show their coats of arms to the class and explain their designs.

Look Into a Crystal Ball

Imagine that you are one of the characters in the selection and that fifteen years have passed since the story occurred. Write a letter to another character in the book whom you haven't seen. Tell him or her what you have been doing since you last saw each other. Relate the content of your letter to the story and mention other characters.

Dear _____ ,

_____

_____

_____

_____

_____

_____

_____

_____

_____

_____

_____

_____

_____

_____

_____

_____

_____

_____

_____

_____

_____

                                    _____ ,

                                    _____

Revise and edit your letter. Write the final copy on separate paper.

Reading Focus   Predictions

Writing Focus   Narrative - personal
Point of view

Teaching Suggestions

To extend the activity, have students take the role of the character to whom they have written and respond to the letter. If two students have read the same selection, have them exchange letters and write responses to each others' letters.

Forget-Me-Not

An epitaph is the writing on a gravestone in memory of the person buried there.

Write an epitaph for one of the characters in your selection.

First think about the traits, habits, and goals for which the character might like to be remembered. Then choose one for the focus of your epitaph.

Write your epitaph. It should ...

   • focus on one of the character's traits, habits, or goals.
   • be in the form of a poem

HERE LIES

L. Red Ridinghood

Although she did her best to be good,
She never really understood
The serious danger
Of talking to a stranger.

Here Lies _____

_____

_____

_____

_____

_____

_____

_____

_____

_____

_____

REVISE ✓ **& EDIT** **COPY**

Revise and edit your epitaph. Write the final copy on separate paper.

Reading Focus   Conclusions - character traits and goals

Writing Focus   Description - poem

Teaching Suggestions

Remind students that their poems need not rhyme.

Some students might enjoy writing their final copies on an original drawing of a tombstone. Display students' work on a bulletin board of "Words to Be Remembered By."

Map It

Choose a character from the selection.   Describe the character by completing the map.

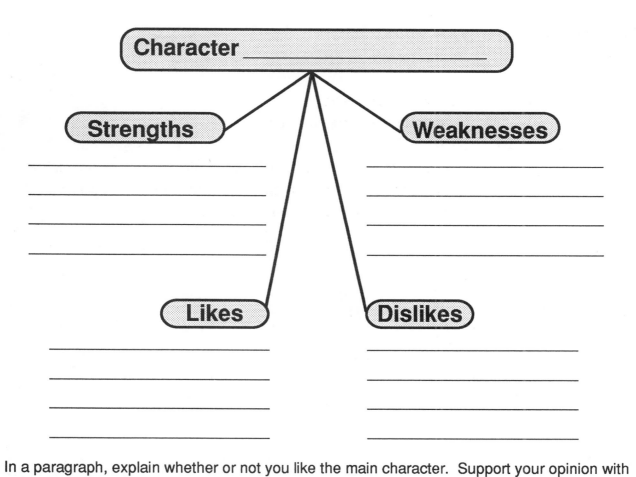

In a paragraph, explain whether or not you like the main character. Support your opinion with examples from the map.

_____

_____

_____

_____

_____

_____

_____

_____

Describe and evaluate a character

Reading Focus   Conclusions - character traits
Judgments

Writing Focus   Persuasion - support opinions

Teaching Suggestions
Encourage students to use specific examples to support their opinions.

I Did It Because ...

Be a character in the selection. Write a letter to another character to explain your motives behind a particular action.

Dear _____,

_____

_____

_____

_____

_____

_____

_____

_____

_____

_____

_____

_____

_____

_____

_____

_____

_____

_____

_____

_____

_____

              _____,

              _____

Revise and edit your letter. Write the final copy on separate paper.

Write a friendly letter

Reading Focus   Conclusions - character motives

Writing Focus   Expository - explanation
Point of view

Teaching Suggestions
To extend the activity, have students take the role of the character
to whom they have written and respond to the letter.

Actions Speak Louder Than Words

Complete the map to show the personality traits of one of the main characters in selection. In each square, write one trait. Under the trait, write two things the character <u>does</u> to reveal that trait.

TRAIT _____

SHOWS BY _____

_____

_____

_____

_____

_____

TRAIT _____

SHOWS BY _____

_____

_____

_____

_____

_____

CHARACTER

_____

TRAIT _____

SHOWS BY _____

_____

_____

_____

_____

_____

TRAIT _____

SHOWS BY _____

_____

_____

_____

_____

_____

WORK ON → NEW PAPER

On separate paper, write a description of the character. Use the information in your map.

Describe a character

Reading Focus   Conclusions - character traits

Writing Focus   Description - character

Teaching Suggestions

Discuss that often writers do not directly state a character's personality traits.   Instead they reveal a character's traits by what the character says, does, and thinks. In this activity, students will identify what the character <u>does</u> to reveal his or her personality traits.   For example, a character might show that he is thoughtful by visiting a sick friend in the hospital instead of playing basketball with friends.

To develop **speaking skills**, have students give a two-minute talk in which they describe their character. Students should use the information in their maps for the content of their speeches.

Dear Mrs. Helpful

Be the main character of your book. Write a letter to Mrs. Helpful to tell her about one of your problems or worries.

ROLE
PLAY

_____

_____

Dear Mrs. Helpful,

_____

_____

_____

_____

_____

_____

_____

_____

_____

_____

_____

_____

_____

_____

_____

_____

_____

_____

_____

_____

Yours truly,

_____

Revise and edit your letter. Write the final copy on separate paper.

Write a friendly letter

Reading Focus   Conclusions - character problems

Writing Focus   Expository - explanation
Point of view

Teaching Suggestions

This response activity is designed to be used alone or in conjunction with the letter-writing activity on page 57. After writing his or her letter to Mrs. Helpful, you may wish to have the student be Mrs. Helpful and do the letter-writing activity on page 57. A second option is to have another student in the class take the role of Mrs. Helpful and do the letter-writing activity on page 57.

Dear Mrs. Helpful (part 2)

Mrs. Helpful always gives her letter writers good advice to help them deal with their problems. Be Mrs. Helpful. Answer the letter.

Mrs. Helpful
Everytown, USA

Dear _____ ,

_____

_____

_____

_____

_____

_____

_____

_____

_____

_____

_____

_____

_____

_____

_____

_____

_____

_____

Very truly yours,

Mrs. Helpful

Revise and edit your letter. Write the final copy on separate paper.

Write a letter of advice

Reading Focus   Judgments

Writing Focus   Persuasion - opinions
Point of view

Teaching Suggestions

This response activity is an optional second part of the Mrs. Helpful letter-writing activity. You may wish to have students complete this letter after they write the one on page 55. Or another student may write this letter in response to a classmate's letter from the activity on page 55.

To develop **speaking skills**, have students present a radio talk show in which book characters call Mrs. Helpful to discuss their problems. The content of the talk show should be based on the problems and solutions students wrote about in their letters.

Music Make-over

Choose a song that you like and rewrite the words to tell about one of the characters in the selection. Your song should have at least two verses.

Song Title

_____

Revise and edit your song. Write the final copy on separate paper.

Write a song

Reading Focus   Conclusions - character traits

Writing Focus   Description - poem

Teaching Suggestions
Encourage students to perform their songs for the class or make a tape recording of them.

Work Wanted!

Imagine that you are the main character of the selection and are looking for a job. First, decide what job you want. Then write a description of yourself for a job application. Describe your best qualities and explain why they make you qualitifed for the position you want. Remember that you are trying to convince someone to hire you.

JOB APPLICATION

For the position of _____

Name _____

Work experience _____

_____

Qualities and abilities _____

_____

_____

Why I should be hired _____

_____

_____

_____

_____

_____

_____

_____

_____

_____

_____

_____

_____

_____

Apply for a job

Reading Focus   Conclusions - character traits

Writing Focus   Persuasion - support opinions
Point of view

Teaching Suggestions

Suggest that students do their prewriting and preliminary drafts on separate paper and write their final copies on the page.

To develop **speaking skills**, have students work in pairs to plan and present job interviews. The interview questions and answers should be based on the information in the job application. A student who has not read the selection may take the part of the employer.

Name

Selection

Personality Poem

Write a cinquain about your favorite character in the selection. A cinquain is a five-line poem that follows a pattern. The notes and example show the pattern for a cinquain about Helen Keller.

Line 1	One word that names the character.............	Helen
Line 2	Two words that describe the character........	Severely disabled
Line 3	Three words that express action.................	Struggled, learned, triumphed
Line 4	Four-word phrase about the character........	Devoted to helping others
Line 5	One word that relates to the character........	Courageous

List words and phrases you might use.

Character _____

Describing Words - Line 2	Action Words - Line 3	Words - Line 5
Phrases - Line 4		

Write your cinquain. Use some of the words and phrases from your chart.

_____

_____ _____

_____ _____ _____

_____

_____

Revise and edit your poem. Write the final copy on separate paper.

Write a poem

Reading Focus   Conclusions - character traits and motives

Writing Focus   Description - poem

Teaching Suggestions
Have students prepare the final copies of their poems for display on a bulletin board of students' work. Some students may enjoy illustrating their cinquains.

Are We Alike?

Choose your favorite character in the selection. Follow the directions to compare yourself to the character.

List three things you like to do.

1. _____

  _____

2. _____

  _____

3. _____

  _____

Be the main character. List three things you like to do.

1. _____

  _____

2. _____

  _____

3. _____

  _____

Write a note to the character that explains how you two are alike or different.

Dear _____,

_____

_____

_____

_____

_____

_____

_____

_____

_____

_____

Write a note

Reading Focus   Comparisons and contrasts
                          Conclusions - character traits

Writing Focus   Expository - comparisons and contrasts

Teaching Suggestions
Explain to students that they will draw conclusions about what their
favorite character likes to do from his or her actions and thoughts.
Encourage students to think of ways they are both similar to and
different from the character.

Be a Psychiatrist

Imagine that you are a psychiatrist for one of the main characters in the selection. You and the character spend today's visit today discussing his or her main problem. Complete the Patient Visit Record for your files.

DATE _____

PATIENT VISIT RECORD

PATIENT _____

What is the patient's main problem?

_____

_____

_____

_____

How successful is the patient in dealing with this problem? Explain why.

_____

_____

_____

_____

_____

_____

What advice did you give the patient?

_____

_____

_____

_____

_____

_____

_____

Analyze a character

Reading Focus   Analysis - character
                      Judgments

Writing Focus   Expository - explanation

Teaching Suggestions
Students may use the questions and their answers as a basis for discussion in a response group.

Some People ...

Write the answers to the questions and discuss them in a response group.

Which character stands out in your mind? Why?

_____

_____

_____

_____

_____

Which character helps you better understand someone you know? Explain why.

_____

_____

_____

_____

_____

Would you like to exchange your life for the life of any character in the selection? Who?
Explain your answer.

_____

_____

_____

_____

_____

_____

_____

_____

_____

Respond to aesthetic questions

Reading Focus   Relate content to personal experiences

Writing Focus   Expository - explanation

Teaching Suggestions
Have students discuss question answers in response groups.

Feature That!

Imagine that you are a columnist for a newspaper. For today's issue, you are to write a feature story about one of the characters in the selection. Your story should tell something that shows the character's best or worst personality trait. Remember that the purpose of a feature story is to entertain as well as inform.

Daily Times

 Revise and edit your feature story. Write the final copy on separate paper.

Reading Focus   Conclusions - character traits

Writing Focus   Description - character

Teaching Suggestions
Review the differences between a news story and a feature story.

To develop **speaking skills**, have the students read aloud their feature stories.

A Few Days in the Life of ...

Be the main character. Write a journal entry for a day at the beginning of the book.

ROLE
PLAY

Date _____

Write a journal entry

Reading Focus   Conclusions - character thoughts and feelings

Writing Focus   Narrative - personal
Point of view

Teaching Suggestions

This response activity is designed to be used alone or in conjunction with the journal writing activity on page 75. After writing a journal entry for a day at the beginning of the book, you may wish to have students complete the activity on page 75 in which they write an entry for a day at the end of the book and then evaluate how the character changed.

A Few Days in the Life Of ... (part 2)

Write a journal entry for a day at the end of the selection. Then write an entry for a day after the selection ends. Discuss how you changed from the beginning to the end of the selection.

Date _____

_____

_____

_____

_____

_____

_____

_____

_____

_____

Date _____

_____

_____

_____

_____

_____

_____

_____

_____

_____

_____

_____

_____

Write journal entries

Reading Focus   Conclusions - character thoughts and feelings
Comparisons

Writing Focus   Narrative - personal
Point of view

Teaching Suggestions
This response activity is an optional second part of the journal - writing activity on page 73.

What's in a Name?

Write an acrostic poem to describe the main character of the selection.   In an acrostic, the first letters of each line form a word, when read from top to bottom.   The word names the topic of the poem. The example shows an acrostic for Martin Luther King, Jr.

> **M**artin Luther King, Jr.,
> **A**merican who fought for
> **R**acial justice
> **T**hrough nonviolent means.
> **I**nspirational leader of the civil rights movement
> **N**onsensically slain by an assassin's bullet.

In each box below, write each letter in the character's name. Then list words that begin with that letter and that you might use in your poem. Use the back of the page for more space.

___	___	___	___	___

Write the letters in the character's name down the page. Then write your poem. Remember that your poem should describe the character.

Revise and edit your poem. Write the final copy on separate paper.

Reading Focus   Conclusions - character traits

Writing Focus   Description - poem

Teaching Suggestions

Some students may wish to illustrate their poems. Compile
poems in a class poetry book.

ROLE PLAY

Be a Time-Traveler

Imagine that you are a time-traveler from the 1990's. You have traveled back in time to the place where the selection occurred. During your visit, you keep careful records of everything that you see.

In your *Time-Travel Log,* describe one thing that you see. For example, you might describe a home, a meal, or a city street. Use descriptive details and colorful words to paint a vivid picture for people living in the 1990's.

TIME-TRAVEL LOG ENTRY 133

DATE _____

PLACE _____

DESCRIPTION _____

_____

_____

_____

_____

_____

_____

_____

_____

_____

_____

_____

_____

_____

_____

_____

_____

_____

_____

_____

_____

Reading Focus   Setting - historical

Writing Focus   Description - vivid details

Teaching Suggestions

To develop **speaking and listening skills**, have students read aloud their descriptions to the class or to a small group. After listening to the description, have the audience identify the words, phrases, and sentences that are most descriptive.

Tell It Like It Was

Answer the questions to tell what you learned from the selection.

When and where did the story occur?

Time _____

Place _____

What important historical events were occurring at that time in history? List one or two.

_____

_____

What new facts and ideas did you learn about that time in history? List information about people, customs, jobs, lifestyle, events, and schools. Look back through the selection.

- _____
_____

- _____
_____

- _____
_____

- _____
_____

- _____
_____

- _____
_____

- _____
_____

- _____
_____

Record new learning

Reading Focus   Distinguish between historical facts and fiction
Identify new learning

Writing Focus   Expository - factual statements

Teaching Suggestions
To develop **speaking skills**, have each student give a short oral
report to explain what he or she learned about the historical period in
which the selection is set.

Through a Looking Glass

ROLE
PLAY

Imagine that you are one of the characters in the selection. You have traveled through time to visit a typical American town in the 1990's. Write a letter to another character at home in the past. Describe how one part of life in the 1990's is different from life as he or she knows it. You may wish to discuss transportation, schools, homes, dress, or leisure activities.

Dear _____ ,

_____

_____

_____

_____

_____

_____

_____

_____

_____

_____

_____

_____

_____

_____

_____

_____

_____

_____

_____

_____

_____ ,

_____

REVISE
✓
& EDIT

COPY

Revise and edit your letter. Write the final copy on separate paper.

Reading Focus   Conclusions - compare and contrast

Writing Focus   Expository - compare and contrast
Point of view

Teaching Suggestions

To extend the response activity, have the student take the part of the character at home and respond to the letter. Or have another student in the class respond to the letter.

To develop **speaking skills**, ask the student to imagine that he or she has returned home and is telling a group of friends about his or her travels. Have the student use the information in the letter as the basis of an explanation of how life in the 1990's is different from life as they know it.

Top Three

Record three of the most interesting new facts that you learned from the selection.

① _____
_____

② _____
_____

③ _____
_____

Choose three of the most interesting new words you learned. For each word, write a meaning and a personal clue to help you remember its meaning.

WORD: _____

MEANING _____
_____
_____

PERSONAL CLUE _____
_____
_____

WORD: _____

MEANING _____
_____
_____

PERSONAL CLUE _____
_____
_____

WORD: _____

MEANING _____
_____
_____

PERSONAL CLUE _____
_____
_____

Record new learning

Reading Focus   Define new words
Identify new learning

Writing Focus   Expository - sentences

Teaching Suggestions

Explain that a personal clue is something from the student's own life that he or she associates with the word. For example, a personal clue for *translucent* might be the window in the door at the dentist's office. Discuss how personal clues help someone remember a word by linking its meaning to something the person already knows.

Name _____

Selection _____

Think It Over

Complete each statement. Write your answers on the lines.

The most interesting part of the selection is _____

because _____

_____

_____

_____

_____

_____

Three of the most interesting new things that I learned from the selection are:

- _____

_____

- _____

_____

- _____

_____

I would/would not recommend this book to a friend for two reasons:

- _____

_____

- _____

_____

Evaluate new learning

Reading Focus   Judgments
Identify new learning

Writing Focus   Persuasion - support opinions

Teaching Suggestions

To develop **speaking skills**, have students give a two-minute oral report in which they share the most interesting new information they gained from reading the selection.

Name

Selection

Enter the Encyclopedia

The editor of the *National Encyclopedia* has asked you to write a short article for an entry in next year's edition. You are to choose a topic that you learned about in your selection, take notes on it, and then write your article. In your article, discuss two main ideas, or important points.

National Encyclopedia

v
o
l

4

My topic _____

Take notes that you will use to write your article. In the left column, write the two main ideas you will discuss in your article. In the right column, list facts that support or illustrate your main ideas.

Article Notes

Main Ideas	Supporting Facts and Examples

WORK ON → **NEW PAPER**

Write your article on separate paper.

Write an encyclopedia entry

Reading Focus   Main ideas and supporting details

Writing Focus   Expository - article
                      Note-taking

Teaching Suggestions

Have students compile their articles in a *Classroom Encyclopedia of Facts.*

To develop **speaking skills**, have students present their information to the class in a news broadcast format. Tell students to imagine that the information in their encyclopedia entries was just discovered and that they are presenting it to the world for the first time.

Be a Poet and Know It

Write a cinquain about the topic of your selection. A cinquain is a five-line poem that follows a pattern. The notes and example show the pattern for a cinquain about pioneers.

Line 1	One word that names the topic................	**Pioneers**
Line 2	Two words that describe the topic............	**Adventurous, industrious**
Line 3	Three words that express action..............	**Traveling, struggling, building**
Line 4	Four-word phrase about the topic............	**Pushing the frontier west**
Line 5	One word that relates to the topic............	**Settlers**

List words and phrases you might use.

Topic _____

Describing Words - Line 2	Action Words - Line 3	Words - Line 5

Phrases - Line 4

Write your cinquain. Use some of the words and phrases from your chart.

Revise and edit your poem. Write the final copy on separate paper.

Write a poem

Reading Focus   Synthesis - main ideas

Writing Focus   Description - poem

Teaching Suggestions

Have students prepare their their final copies for display on a bulletin board of students' work. Some students may wish to write their poems with colored pens; others may enjoy illustrating their cinquains.

Think Back

Write the answers to the questions on the lines.

What was the selection mainly about?

_____

_____

What new information did you learn about the topic?

_____

_____

_____

_____

_____

_____

_____

_____

_____

_____

What do you still want to know about the topic? Write three questions you have.

• _____

_____

• _____

_____

• _____

_____

List three new words you learned.

1 _____   2 _____   3 _____

Reading Focus   Main idea and details
Judgments

Writing Focus   Expository - main idea and supporting details

Teaching Suggestions
To extend the response activity, have students use classroom
resources or library reference books to answer their questions.

The Facts of Life

Complete the map with the six most important events in the life of the subject of the selection. List the events in chronological order. Then write a summary that tells the main events in the person's life.

EVENTS　　**Person:** _____

Event 1 _____
_____
_____

Event 2 _____
_____
_____

Event 3 _____
_____
_____

Event 4 _____
_____
_____

Event 5 _____
_____
_____

Event 6 _____
_____

WORK ON　→　**NEW PAPER**

Write your summary on separate paper.

Map a character's life

Reading Focus   Main events
                      Sequence

Writing Focus   Narrative - summary

Teaching Suggestions

To develop **speaking skills**, have students use their maps to give a short report about the life of the subject of their selection.

Make Connections

Write the answers to the questions and discuss them in a response group.

What did you learn about the qualities and methods of successful people?

_____

_____

_____

_____

_____

How did the book give you a better understanding of human nature?

_____

_____

_____

_____

_____

How can you use what you learned in your own life?

_____

_____

_____

_____

_____

_____

_____

_____

_____

Respond to aesthetic questions

Reading Focus   Theme

Writing Focus   Expository - explanation

Teaching Suggestions

Have students discuss question answers in response groups.

Say It with a Symbol

A symbol is something that stands for something else. For example, a lion stands for courage, the Statue of Liberty is a symbol of the United States, and the color green symbolizes envy.

In the box, draw a symbol you associate with the subject of the selection.   Your symbol may represent the person's qualities, contributions, occupation, or interests.

SUBJECT OF THE SELECTION _____

Now write a paragraph to explain why the symbol represents the person.

Reading Focus   Conclusions - character traits

Writing Focus   Expository - explanation

Teaching Suggestions

Suggest that students draw their symbols on art paper and write a revised and edited copy of their paragraphs under the symbol.

To develop **speaking skills**, have each student draw a symbol to represent himself or herself and then explain to the class why the symbol is appropriate.

Personality Map

Complete the map to describe the subject of the selection. Then use the information in the
map to write a description of the person.

STRENGTHS	WEAKNESSES

PERSON _____

PERSONALITY TRAITS	CONTRIBUTIONS

WORK
ON

NEW
PAPER

Write your character description on separate paper.

Plan and write a character sketch

Reading Focus   Conclusions - character traits

Writing Focus   Description - character sketch

Teaching Suggestions

Remind students that they will have to draw conclusions to complete the map because most writers don't directly state a character's strengths, weaknesses, and traits. Instead, they reveal the character's personality by the things he or she does, says, and thinks.

Who's Who?

ROLE PLAY

Imagine that you are a contributing writer for *Who's Who - Then and Now*, a reference book that gives information about famous people. Your job is to write an entry for the subject of the selection. Fill out the form below. Then use the information to write the entry.

Who's Who Then and Now

Name _____

Year born _____   Place of birth _____   Year died _____

Education _____

_____

Occupation _____

Honors_____

_____

Accomplishments (brief description) _____

_____

_____

Use the information above to write your entry. Use separate paper if you need more space.

_____

_____

_____

_____

_____

_____

_____

_____

_____

_____

REVISE & EDIT   COPY

Revise and edit your entry. Write the final copy on separate paper.

Write a *Who's Who* entry

Reading Focus   Character - facts

Writing Focus   Expository - article
Point of view

Teaching Suggestions
After students revise and edit their entries, have them write their final copies in a form that will enable them to compile the entries in a classroom *Who's Who of Famous People.*

Make a Strong Case

Write a business letter to convince the *Hall of Fame* board to invite the subject of your selection to be in the *Hall of Fame*. Tell who the person is and explain why he or she is worthy of being included in the *Hall of Fame*. Discuss the contributions the person has made and any obstacles he or she has overcome.

_____

_____

Hall of Fame Board
111 Main Street
Washington City   NY

Dear Board Members:

_____

_____

_____

_____

_____

_____

_____

_____

_____

_____

_____

_____

_____

_____

_____

_____

_____

_____

_____

_____

_____

_____

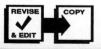

Revise and edit your letter. Write the final copy on separate paper.

Write a business letter

Reading Focus   Summary

Judgments

Writing Focus   Persuasion - support opinions

Teaching Suggestions

To develop **speaking skills**, have students read aloud their letters to a small group who pretend to be the Hall of Fame Board. After hearing the letter, have the board members vote to decide whether to include the subject in the Hall of Fame.

Play the Role

You have been chosen to play the lead role in a production of the play you just read. Your director wants you to think about how you will play your part. She has asked you to choose the character's most important trait and explain how you will reveal that trait as you play the part. You are to suggest scenes and lines in the play that you will use. Complete the *Acting Plan* for the director.

ACTING PLAN

CHARACTER _____

MOST IMPORTANT TRAIT _____

_____

_____

_____

_____

_____

_____

_____

_____

_____

_____

_____

_____

_____

_____

_____

_____

_____

_____

_____

_____

Write an acting plan

Reading Focus   Conclusions - character traits

Writing Focus   Expository - explanation

Teaching Suggestions

To develop **speaking skills**, have students choose some of the character's lines mentioned in their Acting Plans and read or act them out as described in their plans.

All the World's a Stage

Imagine that you are the set designer for the play you just read. Design the set for your favorite scene. Include backdrop and props in your sketch.

SET DESIGN FOR SCENE _____

On separate paper, write a description of the set for the stage hands who will build it.

Design and describe a stage set

Reading Focus   Setting

Writing Focus   Description - stage setting

Teaching Suggestions
Some students may wish to draw the final copy of their set designs on art paper. Display designs along with revised and edited versons of their descriptions on a bulletin board of students' work.

In Character

Imagine that you are the director of a production of the play you just read. You have chosen actors to play each role and now have to let each one know how you "see" the character. Choose one character. Use the form to write a description of the way you want the character played.

ROLE PLAY

SKETCH FOR _____

(CHARACTER)

PHYSICAL APPEARANCE _____

_____

_____

_____

_____

_____

KEY PERSONALITY TRAITS _____

_____

TO BE REVEALED BY _____

_____

_____

_____

_____

_____

MANNERISMS AND WAY OF TALKING _____

_____

_____

_____

_____

Write a character sketch

Reading Focus   Conclusions - character traits, actions, and mannerisms

Writing Focus   Description - character

Teaching Suggestions

To develop **speaking skills**, have students work in small groups to present a scene from the play. Have students take the role of the character they described and use their descriptions to rehearse and polish their parts.

What's the Point?

Write the answers to the questions and discuss them in a response group.

Of what does the folktale make you think?

_____

_____

_____

_____

What do you think the writer is trying to teach us with this folktale?

_____

_____

_____

_____

How can you use the writer's lesson in your own life?

_____

_____

_____

_____

_____

_____

_____

_____

Respond to aesthetic questions

Reading Focus   Theme
                      Relate poem to personal experience

Writing Focus   Expository - explanation

Teaching Suggestions
Have students discuss question answers in response groups.

Who Dunnit?

Write the answers to the questions.

WHAT IS THE PROBLEM, OR MYSTERY?

_____

_____

_____

Mystery in Milwaukee

The Case of the Missing Diamonds

Midnight Mysteries

HOW DOES THE WRITER DRAW YOU INTO THE MYSTERY?

_____

_____

_____

_____

_____

AT WHAT POINT IN THE STORY DID YOU KNOW THE SOLUTION?

_____

_____

WHAT IS THE SOLUTION?

_____

_____

_____

IS THE SOLUTION BELIEVABLE? EXPLAIN YOUR ANSWER.

_____

_____

_____

_____

WOULD YOU RECOMMEND THIS MYSTERY TO A FRIEND? EXPLAIN YOUR ANSWER.

_____

_____

_____

Analyze and evaluate a mystery

Reading Focus   Analysis - elements of a mystery
Judgments

Writing Focus   Expository - explanation

Teaching Suggestions
Have students discuss their answers in response groups.

And the Culprit Is ...

Write the answers to the questions.

What is the mystery?

_____

_____

_____

How does the main character solve the mystery?

How does he or she gather clues?

_____

_____

What clues does he or she gather?

_____

_____

What logical conclusion does he or she draw from the clues?

_____

_____

Does the writer give misleading clues? If yes, how did they affect your understanding and enjoyment of the mystery?

_____

_____

Reading Focus   Analysis - elements of a mystery

Writing Focus   Expository - explanation

Teaching Suggestions
Have students discuss their answers in response groups.

The Case of ...

Plan and write a short mystery story. Your main character should be the same one as in the mystery you read and use the same method to solve the mystery as he or she did in the selection. Plan the plot of your mystery by completing the map. Then write your mystery.

SETTING   When and where does the story take place?

_____

_____

MAIN CHARACTERS   Who are the main characters?

_____

_____

PROBLEM   What is the mystery?

_____

_____

RISING ACTION

How will the main character gather evidence?

_____

_____

What evidence will he or she gather?

_____

_____

CLIMAX   How and when will the main character know the solution to the mystery?

_____

_____

CONCLUSION   What is the solution to the mystery?

_____

_____

WORK ON → NEW PAPER   Write your story on separate paper.

Write a mystery

Reading Focus   Plot - elements
Extend thinking about mysteries

Writing Focus   Narrative - short story

Teaching Suggestions
To develop **speaking skills**, have students work in small groups to present their mystery stories as radio plays.

Second Thoughts

Follow the directions to develop your own meaning from the poem.

Reread the poem. As you do, write down what comes to your mind. Your comments may be words and phrases, questions, or sentences.

_____

_____

_____

_____

_____

_____

_____

Read the poem once more. Write down what you are thinking this time as you read it.

_____

_____

_____

_____

_____

_____

_____

_____

_____

_____

Explain what meaning the poem has for you.

_____

_____

_____

_____

_____

Derive personal meaning from a poem

Reading Focus   Theme
Relate poem to personal experience

Writing Focus   Expository - explanation

Teaching Suggestions
Before students begin, explain that there are no right or wrong answers to the questions. The purpose of the activity is to have each person derive his or her own meaning from the poem.

After students have completed the activity, have them form response groups and share their thoughts about their poems.

Think Along

Choose your favorite verse from the poem. Write one line from the verse in each shaded area. Underneath, write a personal response to the line. A response is any comment or thought that comes to your mind as you read and think about the words. It may be one or two words, a question, or a sentence.

Favorite Poems

Line _____

My response _____

_____

Line _____

My response _____

_____

Line _____

My response _____

_____

Line _____

My response _____

_____

Line _____

My response _____

_____

What do you like best about this poem? _____

_____

Respond freely to a poem

Reading Focus   Relate poem to personal experience

Writing Focus   Expository - free response

Teaching Suggestions

Before students begin, explain that there are no right or wrong answers. The purpose of the response activity is to have each person derive his or her own meaning from the poem.

To develop **speaking skills,** have each student rehearse his or her favorite stanza of the poem and read it aloud to the class.

Get a Word In

Choose three new words from the selection and complete a vocabulary map for each one.

Word _____

Meaning _____

_____

Example _____

_____

Sentence _____

_____

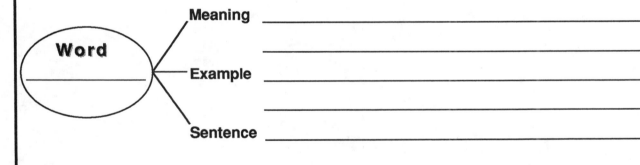

Word _____

Meaning _____

_____

Example _____

_____

Sentence _____

_____

Word _____

Meaning _____

_____

Example _____

_____

Sentence _____

_____

Reading Focus   Define and new use words

Writing Focus   Expository - sentences

Teaching Suggestions
Encourage students to draw on their own experiences to give examples that illustrate each word's meaning. Also remind them that each sentence should indicate that they understand the meaning of the new vocabulary word.

Words Make the World Go 'Round

Choose three new words from the selection and complete a vocabulary chart for each one.

New Word: _____

Synonym or short definition: _____

_____

Personal clue: _____

_____

Sentence: _____

_____

New Word: _____

Synonym or short definition: _____

_____

Personal clue: _____

_____

Sentence: _____

_____

New Word: _____

Synonym or short definition: _____

_____

Personal clue: _____

_____

Sentence: _____

_____

Complete vocabulary charts

Reading Focus   Define and use new words
Relate word meaning to personal experiences

Writing Focus   Expository - sentences

Teaching Suggestions
Explain that a personal clue is something from the student's own life that he or she associates with the word. For example, a personal clue for *entice* might be the memory of trying to draw a bird to one's hand by holding out birdseed. Discuss how personal clues help a person remember a word by linking its meaning to something the person already knows.

Name

Selection

Be Convincing!

Imagine that you are a person who sells books. Write the sales talk you would give parents to persuade them to buy the selection for their children.

Revise and edit your sales talk. Write the final copy on separate paper.

Reading Focus   Judgments

Writing Focus   Persuasion - support opinions

Teaching Suggestions

To develop **speaking and listening skills**, ask students to give their sales talks to the class. Students in the audience should take the role of parents. After hearing a sales talk, have the audience discuss whether they are convinced to buy the selection for their children.

Tell It Like It Is

Complete the map to tell what you thought about the selection.

Title _____

What I Liked

_____
_____
_____
_____
_____
_____
_____
_____
_____
_____
_____
_____
_____
_____

What I Didn't Like

_____
_____
_____
_____
_____
_____
_____
_____
_____
_____
_____
_____
_____
_____
_____
_____

General Rating

I thought the selection was _____ .

Dull   Fair   Good   Wonderful   Fantastic

Complete a map

Reading Focus   Judgments

Writing Focus   Persuasion - opinions

Teaching Suggestions
Encourage students to give specific examples of what they like and dislike about the selection.

Name

Selection

Make the Picture Clear

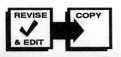

Imagine that you are the author of the selection. You are to decide what picture you want on the selection cover. This picture should give readers an idea of what the book is mainly about as well as interest them in reading it. First sketch your picture. Then write a description of the picture for an illustrator. Include specific details so the illustrator can draw exactly what you have in mind.

Revise and edit your description. Write your final copy on separate paper.

Reading Focus   Main idea

Writing Focus   Description - details

Teaching Suggestions

Some students may enjoy taking the role of the illustrator and drawing the picture in final form.

To develop **speaking skills**, have students read aloud their descriptions to a classmate or family member. The listener will draw the picture. Students should then use the pictures to evaluate their descriptions and revise them as necessary.

How Does It Rate?

Write the answers to the questions.

Evaluation Form

Circle the words that best describe the selection.

fascinating	wonderful	boring	action-packed	so-so	fun
slow-moving	too short	too long	easy-to-read	difficult	great

Add three of your own words to describe the selection.

_____   _____   _____

What did you like best about the selection? Explain your answer.

_____

_____

_____

What did you like least about the selection? Explain your answer.

_____

_____

_____

What kind of person should read this selection? Explain your answer.

_____

_____

Would you read another book by this author? Explain your answer.

_____

_____

On a scale of 1 to 10, what overall rating would you give this book? _____

Reading Focus   Judgments

Writing Focus   Persuasion - support opinions

Teaching Suggestions
Have students who have read the same selection share their
opinions in a small group discussion.

A Funny Thing Happened

Be the main character of the selection.   Retell the funniest incident in the story to your best friend. Include only the most important things that happened.

Revise and edit your retelling. Write the final copy on separate paper.

Retell a humorous event

Reading Focus   Summary - story event

Writing Focus   Narrative - sequence
Point of view

Teaching Suggestions

To develop **speaking skills**, have students take the role of the main character and retell the humorous event to the class or to a small group.

Buy This Book!

Be the owner of a book store. Ceate an advertisement to persuade people to buy and read the selection. In your ad include the selection title and author, information to persuade someone to read the selection, and an illustration.

Create an advertisement

Reading Focus   Judgments

Writing Focus   Persuasion - advertising copy

Teaching Suggestions

Have students use the response page to plan and sketch their ads and then draw their final copies on art paper. Compile completed ads in a notebook to which students may refer when selecting books to read.

To develop **speaking skills**, have students use their ads to create 30-second television commericals to sell their books.

Say What You Think

Write the answers to the questions and discuss them in a response group.

What is one thing in the story that sticks in your mind? Why is this important to you?

_____

_____

_____

_____

_____

Chose one character. What does the character make you think about or remind you of? Explain why.

_____

_____

_____

_____

_____

Of what in your own life does the story make you think?

_____

_____

_____

_____

_____

_____

_____

_____

Respond to aesthetic questions

Reading Focus   Relate content to personal experiences

Writing Focus   Expository - explanation

Teaching Suggestions
Have students discuss question answers in response groups.

Meet the Press

The author of your selection is holding a press conference. Imagine that you are a reporter for your local newspaper and will attend the press conference. Write six questions you will ask the author.

ROLE PLAY

1. _____

_____

2. _____

_____

3. _____

_____

4. _____

_____

5. _____

_____

6. _____

_____

Choose one of your questions. Be the author and answer the question.

_____

_____

_____

_____

_____

Write interview questions

Reading Focus   Author's purpose

Writing Focus   Expository - interview questions and answers

Teaching Suggestions

If two or more students read the selection and wrote interview questions, have them trade papers and write answers to each other's questions.

To develop **speaking skills**, have students plan and present a press conference based on the interview questions. Students who haven't read the selection may play reporters who ask the questions.

In Praise of Authors

Write a letter to the author explaining why you enjoyed or didn't enjoy the selection. Use examples from the selection to support your opinion.

_____

_____

Dear _____,

_____

_____

_____

_____

_____

_____

_____

_____

_____

_____

_____

_____

_____

_____

_____

Yours truly,

_____

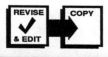

Revise and edit your letter. Write the final copy on separate paper.

Write a friendly letter

Reading Focus   Judgments

Writing Focus   Persuasion - support opinions
Point of view

Teaching Suggestions
Encourage students to write their final copies on stationery and send them to the author.

On a Scale of 1 to 5

Read each statement and then rate your reaction to it. Circle the number that most describes your feeling. Then write a short explanation for your rating. Use examples from the selection to support your opinions.

As I read the book, I felt as though I were an eyewitness to the action.

Strongly Disagree   Strongly Agree

1 2 3 4 5

Explanation: _____

_____

The writer creates vivid pictures in words.

Strongly Disagree   Strongly Agree

1 2 3 4 5

Explanation: _____

_____

As I read, I could identify with the feelings of one of the main characters.

Strongly Disagree   Strongly Agree

1 2 3 4 5

Explanation: _____

_____

I would like to read more by this author.

Strongly Disagree   Strongly Agree

1 2 3 4 5

Explanation: _____

_____

Overall Rating for Selection

1	**2**	**3**	**4**	**5**
Dull	Fair	Good	Enjoyable	Great

Evaluate a selection

Reading Focus   Judgments
                       Analysis - writer's style

Writing Focus   Persuasion - support opinions

Teaching Suggestions
Encourage students to support their opinions with specific examples from the selection.

Have students who have read the same selection discuss their opinions in small groups.

Critic's Corner

Imagine that you are the book reviewer for a city newspaper. Write a review of the selection. Your review should:

- name the title and author
- state the story problem in one or two sentences
- discuss anything that is unusual about the selection
- explain why you enjoyed or didn't enjoy the selection

_____
_____
_____
_____
_____
_____
_____
_____
_____
_____
_____
_____
_____
_____
_____
_____
_____
_____
_____
_____
_____

REVISE ✔ & EDIT **COPY ➡** Revise and edit your review. Write the final copy on separate paper.

Reading Focus   Judgments
Plot - problem

Writing Focus   Persuasion - support opinions

Teaching Suggestions

Compile reviews in a *Critic's Corner Notebook* to which students
can refer when they are selecting books to read.

To develop **speaking skills**, have students turn their reviews into
30-second radio commercials that they will present to the class.

Name

Selection

Express Your Feelings

How did the selection make you feel? In the box, write words and phrases that describe your feelings.

Write a poem that describes how the selection made you feel. Use some of your ideas above.

Revise and edit your poem. Write the final copy on separate paper

Write a poem

Reading Focus   Express personal reactions to a selection

Writing Focus   Description - poem

Teaching Suggestions

Remind students that poems do not have to rhyme nor follow any set pattern.

Name

Selection

What Next?

Imagine that the selection you read was made into a movie. The movie was such a success that the producer wants to make a sequel and has asked you to write it. Remember that a sequel is a complete story by itself but carries on from where a previous story ends.
Plan the plot for your sequel by completing the map.

Setting

Where?_____

When? _____

Main Characters

_____

_____

Problem

_____

_____

EVENTS   **Rising Action**

_____

_____

_____

_____

_____

_____

_____

_____

Solution

_____

_____

Write your sequel on separate paper.

Write a sequel

Reading Focus   Extend thinking beyond the selection

Writing Focus   Narrative - short story
Mapping - plot

Teaching Suggestions

Have students complete the plot map to plan their sequels and then write their rough drafts and final copies on separate paper.

To develop **speaking skills**, have students use their plot maps to tell their sequels to the class or to a small group of classmates.